Make it easy...

English

Age 4-5

Lynn Huggins-Cooper

The letter s

The letter s looks like a snake.

It makes the same sound as a snake. **Sssssssssssssssssss ssssss!**

I Circle the things that start with s.

a   b   c   d

II Write s in each space. Then draw a picture of each thing.

a ____nake   b ____oap   c ____wing

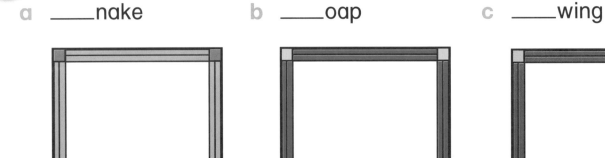

2

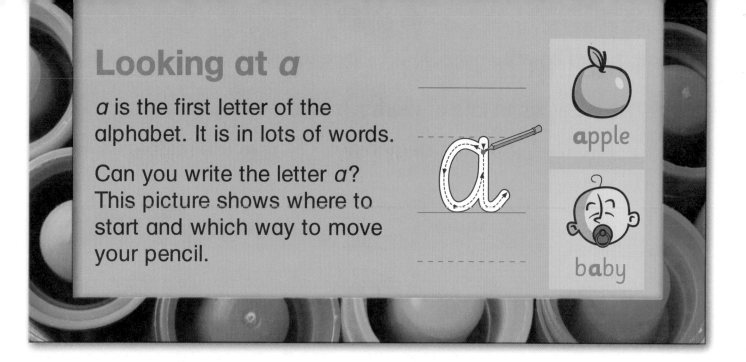

Looking at a

a is the first letter of the alphabet. It is in lots of words.

Can you write the letter *a*? This picture shows where to start and which way to move your pencil.

apple

baby

I Colour the pictures in each set that start with *a*.

a
apple

b
leaf

c
ant

d
alligator

orange

acorn

ladybird

cat

II Write an *a* on each apple.

3

Finding *i*

The letter *i* is in lots of words.

	At the beginning:	In the middle:
	igloo	finish
	iron	fish

I **Circle the words that start with *i*.**

a ink   pencil   book

b lolly   ice cream   sweets

c country   sea   island

d pan   iron   cup

e flower   ivy   grass

f in   out   up

g think   idea   try

h ill   well   sick

i warm   hot   icy

j scratch   itch   stroke

II **Write an *i* in these words.**

a

p___nk

b

b___n

c

m___lk

d

dr___ll

e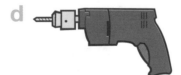

st___nk

f

___dea

The letter *t*

The letter *t* looks like a cross.

Can you write the letter *t*? This picture shows where to start and which way to move your pencil.

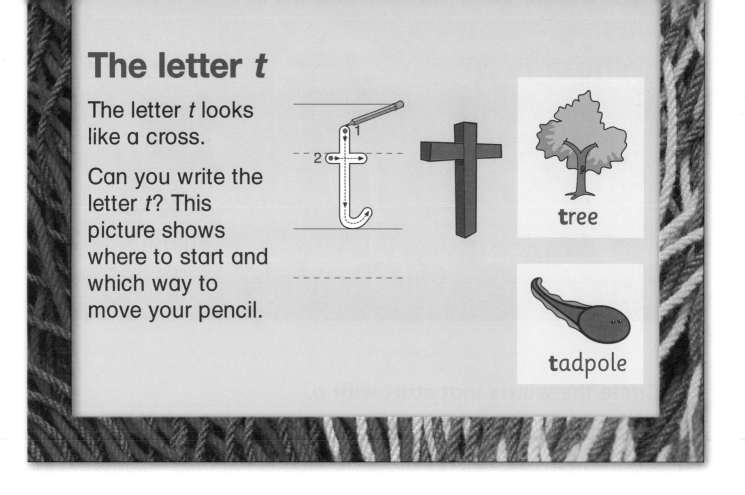

tree

tadpole

I   **Circle the things that start with *t*.**

a   b   c   d

car   tiger   television   chair

train   elephant   radio   table

II   **Write a *t* carefully on each train carriage.**

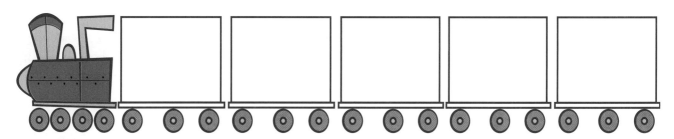

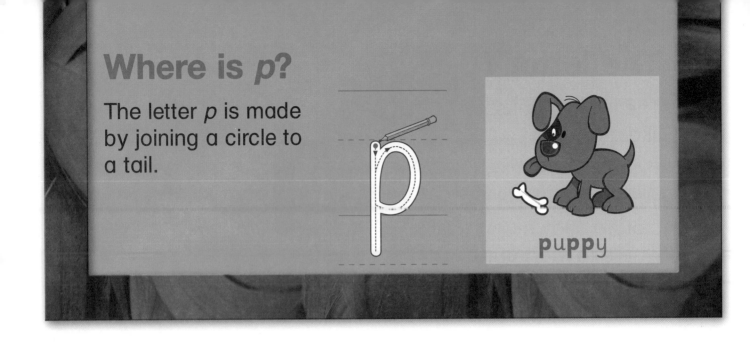

Where is p?

The letter p is made by joining a circle to a tail.

puppy

Circle the words that start with p.

a draw play dance

b pool chair cream

c red green pink

d pipe soap water

e dish pan plate

f post letter card

g hand paw foot

h pen ink ruler

i rubber dice pencil

j book plants comic

Now add the p to finish each word. Look at the big p at the top of the page to help you.

a ____ink

b ____at

c hel____

d ____ut

e co____y

f ____ull

g s ____ell

h ____itch

i ____ot

j ____it

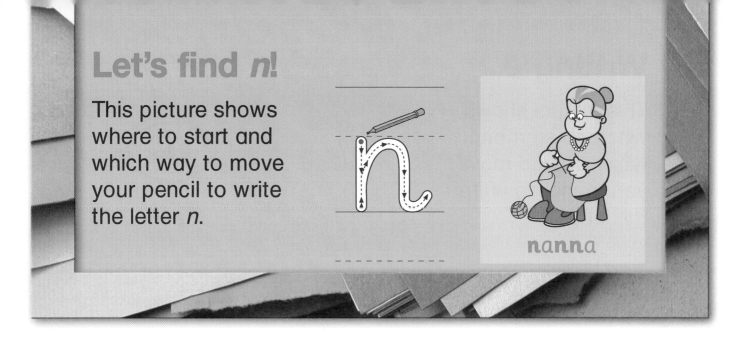

Let's find *n*!

This picture shows where to start and which way to move your pencil to write the letter *n*.

nanna

Draw a line to join the *n* word to the picture.

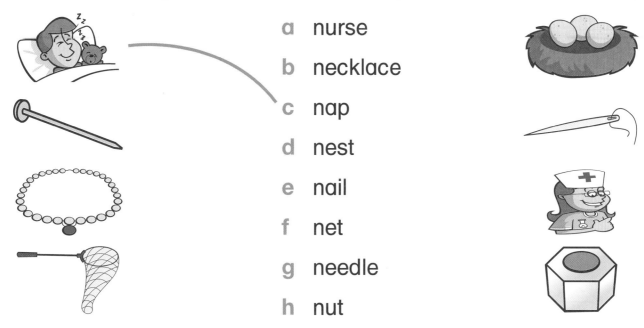

a   nurse

b   necklace

c   nap

d   nest

e   nail

f   net

g   needle

h   nut

Write an *n* on each bead of the necklace.

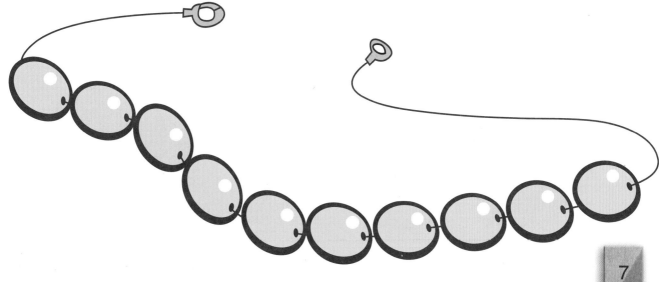

Writing e

This picture shows where to start and which way to move your pencil to write the letter e.

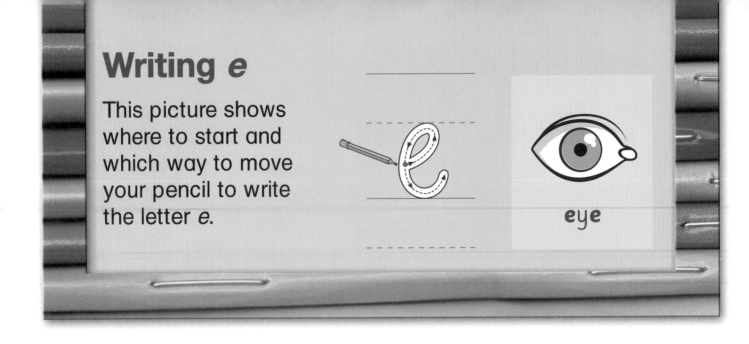

eye

I Colour the buns for the elephant to eat. She only likes words that start with *e*! Write the words you find below.

ball   earth   foot   eel

egg   eight   kind   ear   eat

a _____   d _____

b _____   e _____

c _____   f _____

II Write an *e* on each **e**gg.

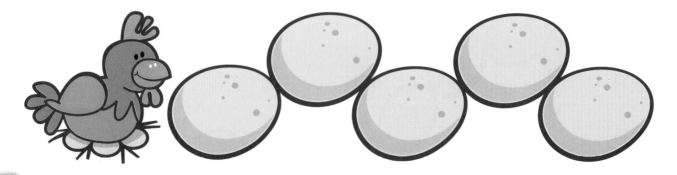

Finding c

This picture shows where to start and which way to move your pencil to write the letter c.

cat

cup

Draw the things listed below in the cat shape.

a cat

b caterpillar

c cap

d car

e carrot

f cup

g coat

Copy these words. Use your best handwriting!

a can _____

b car _____

c cat _____

d cab _____

e cap _____

f call _____

g carry _____

h cake _____

i card _____

j castle _____

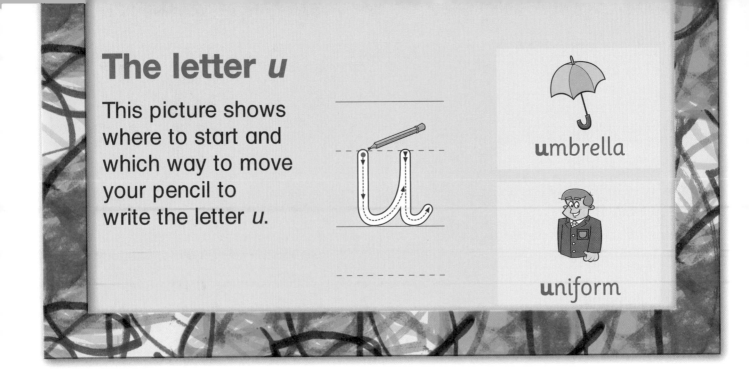

The letter *u*

This picture shows where to start and which way to move your pencil to write the letter *u*.

umbrella

uniform

I Colour in the raindrops that show *u* words. Then write them out.

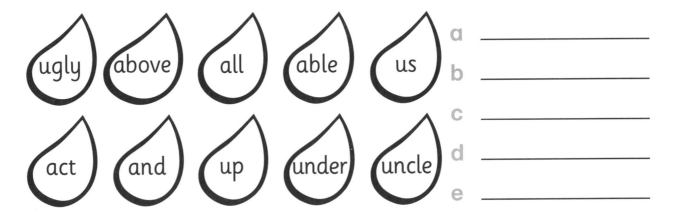

ugly   above   all   able   us

act   and   up   under   uncle

a _____
b _____
c _____
d _____
e _____

II Copy the words onto the umbrellas.

unload

unlucky

unlock

untie

The letter o

The letter *o* looks like a ball. It is a circle shape.

This picture shows where to start and which way to move your pencil to write the letter *o*.

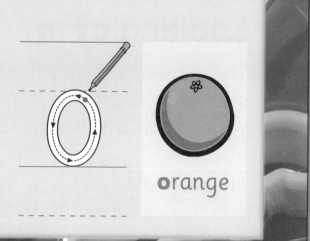

orange

I Look for the *o* words on the owl. Write them on the mice.

art out

write odd

old our

horse oar

ocean

a

b

c

d

e

f

II Fill in the *o* to finish these words.

a s____ld

b sp____t

c c____ld

d w____rld

e m____ney

f p____p

g b____x

h w____rk

i b____w

Looking at *m*

This picture shows where to start and which way to move your pencil to write the letter *m*.

mummy

I Circle the five words beginning with *m*. Write the words below.

a _____

b _____

c _____

d _____

e _____

arrow   medal

map   monkey

mud   glass   baby

ball   mouse

II Draw 6 things that start with *m* in the boxes below.

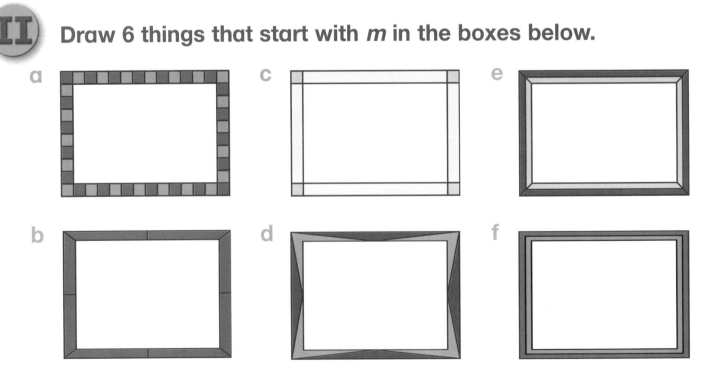

a

b

c

d

e

f

Where is *r*?

This picture shows where to start and which way to move your pencil to write the letter *r*.

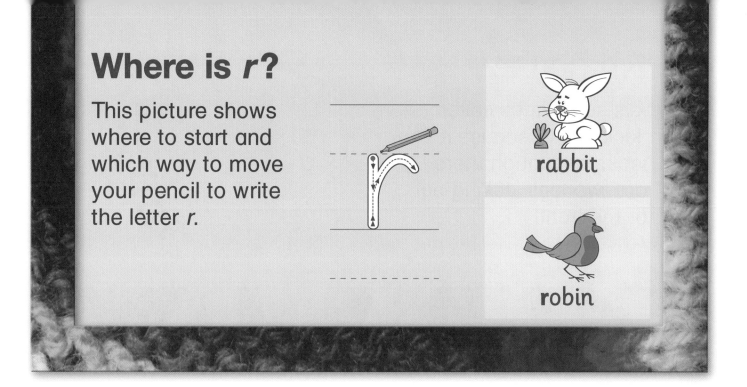

rabbit

robin

I **Circle the word in each set beginning with *r*.**

a rain   snow   wind   d rabbit   horse   duck

b string   chain   rope   e pasta   rice   soup

c green   yellow   red   f walk   crawl   run

II **Draw six things beginning with *r*.**

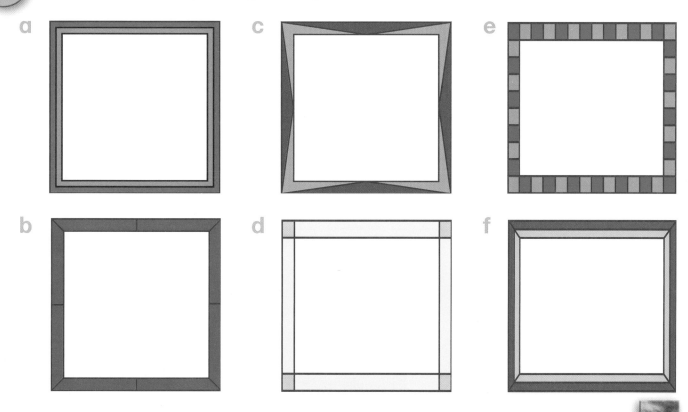

a   c   e

b   d   f

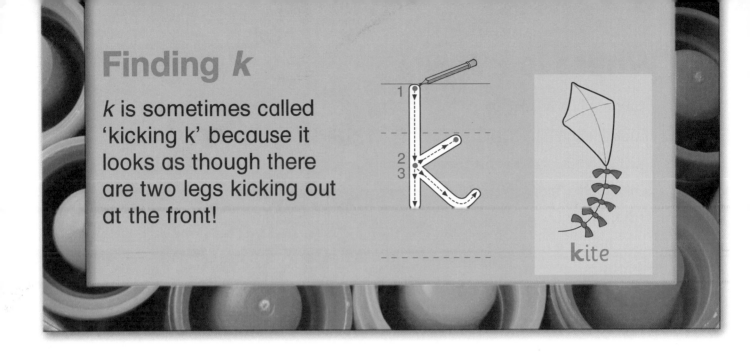

Finding k

k is sometimes called 'kicking k' because it looks as though there are two legs kicking out at the front!

kite

Draw a line from the words that start with k to the kangaroo. Then write the words you find in the spaces below.

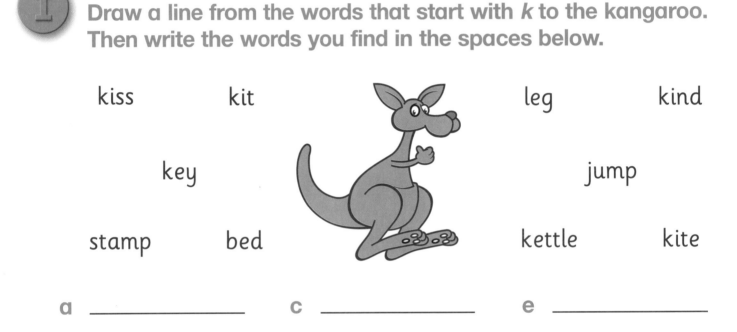

kiss   kit   leg   kind

    key   jump

stamp   bed   kettle   kite

a _____   c _____   e _____

b _____   d _____   f _____

Write a k in these words. Draw a picture for each word.

a cloc___   b ___itten   c ___ettle

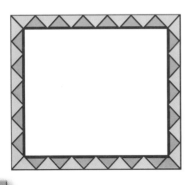      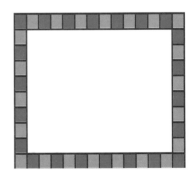

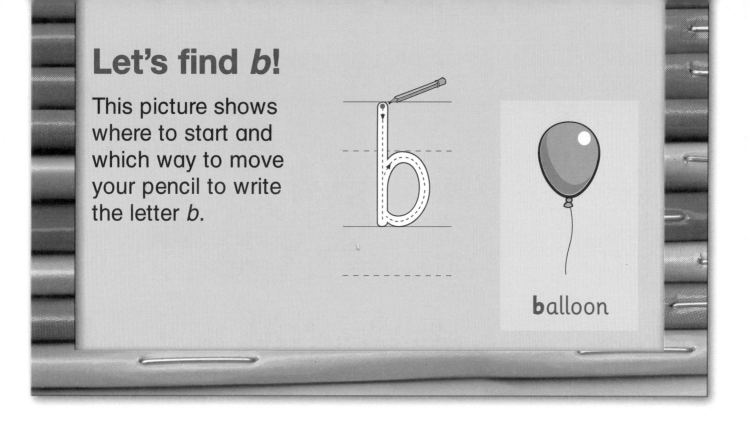

Let's find *b*!

This picture shows where to start and which way to move your pencil to write the letter *b*.

balloon

I Copy all the words that begin with *b* inside the balloon shape.

a kid, child, boy

b bad, good, nice

c kite, bat, game

d bus, car, train

e ant, bug, fly

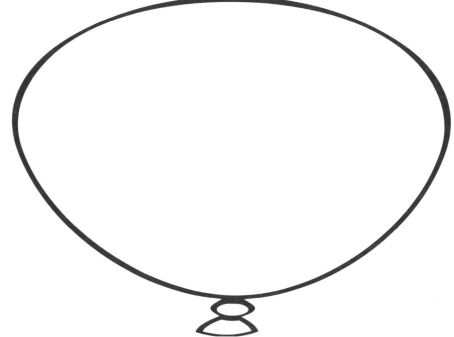

II Write the letter *b* to finish the words.

a tu＿＿

b ＿＿ox

c ＿＿end

d ＿＿ank

e ＿＿a＿＿y

f ＿＿in

g ＿＿o＿＿

h jo＿＿

i ＿＿un

The letter *d*

The letter *d* looks like a back to front *b*! Lots of people get mixed up at first. Try to remember by saying to yourself '*b* has a belly' so you remember that the round bit sticks out in front on a *b*, not a *d*!

daddy

Draw a line to join the *d* words to the dog. Then write the words underneath.

drum   deer   duck   cat

      hat   doll

dress   purse   candle   door

a _____   c _____   e _____

b _____   d _____   f _____

Write the letter *d* in the spaces carefully to finish the words.

a ma__e   d bo__y   g car__

b she__   e __rain   h __esk

c __isc   f __oll   i han__le

16

Finding l

The letter l is easy to write. It is just a line straight down with a little curl at the bottom.

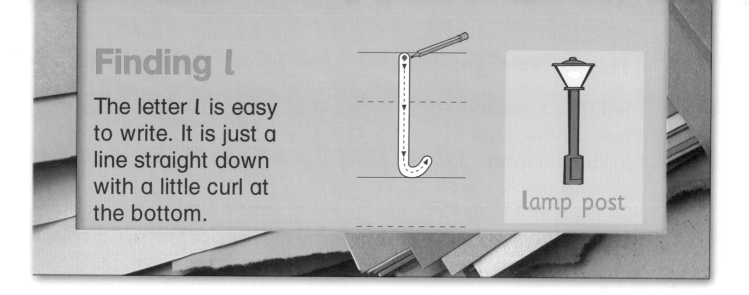

lamp post

Write an l carefully on each leaf.

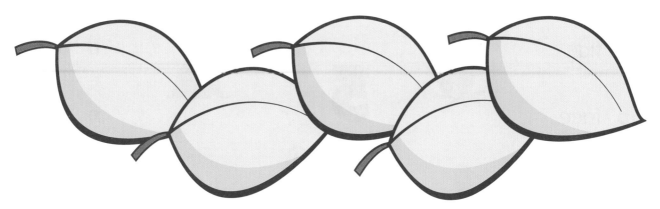

Circle the things that start with l. Tick the words as you find each thing.

a lamp ☐

b letter ☐

c light ☐

d lock ☐

e lady ☐

f lemon ☐

g ladybird ☐

h lollipop ☐

i lorry ☐

j lamb ☐

The letter f

The letter *f* is like a cross, or the letter *t*. You draw a long stick first, and then cross it with a shorter stick.

feather

I Draw a line to join the pictures to the word.

a flag

b face

c fin

d finger

e five

f fire

II Draw something that starts with *f* on each fish shape. Then write the word.

a

b

c

d

e

f

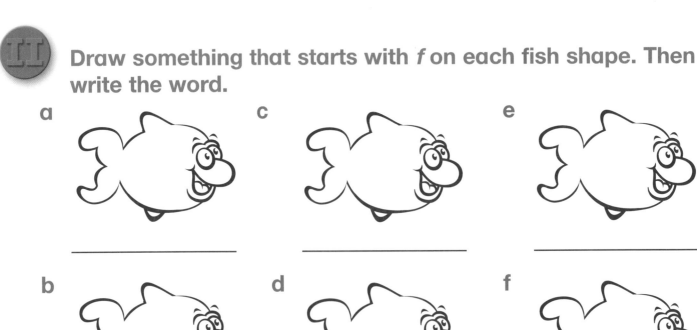

Writing lower case letters

a b c d e f g h i j k l m
n o p q r s t u v w x y z

Write **carefully**, so people can read what you say.

I Copy these letters across the page until the line is full. Remember to check that you are writing the letter in the correct way.

a S _____

b a _____

c c _____

d e _____

II Now copy these groups of letters across the page until the line is full. Do you recognise all of the letters?

a bpbp _____

b fgfg _____

c pqpq _____

d zzzz _____

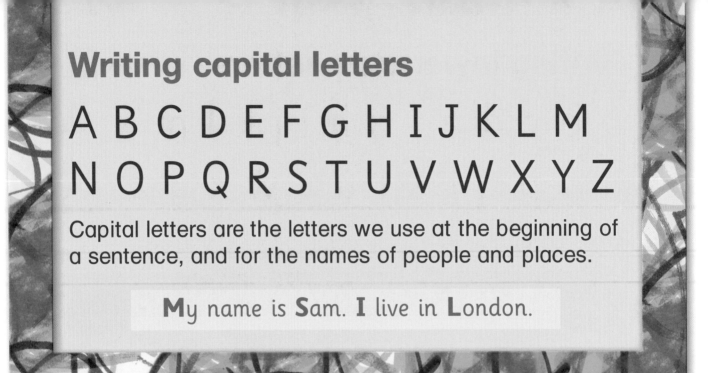

Writing capital letters

A B C D E F G H I J K L M
N O P Q R S T U V W X Y Z

Capital letters are the letters we use at the beginning of a sentence, and for the names of people and places.

My name is **S**am. **I** live in **L**ondon.

I Copy the capital letters across the page until the line is full. These letters are made up from straight lines, so they are not too hard!

a A _____

b E _____

c K _____

d T _____

II Now try these. These capitals have some curves or rounded parts. Copy the letters across the page until the line is full.

a O _____

b Q _____

c S _____

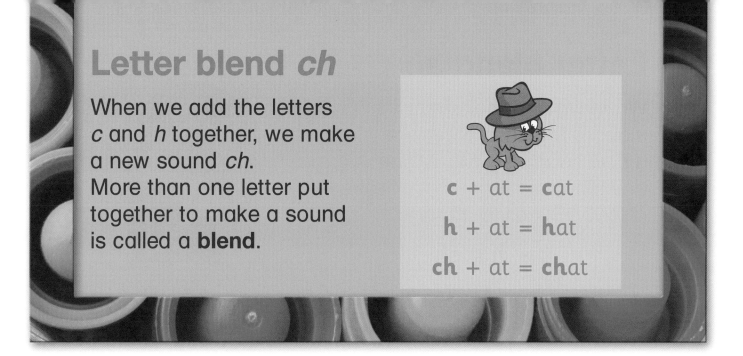

Letter blend *ch*

When we add the letters *c* and *h* together, we make a new sound *ch*.
More than one letter put together to make a sound is called a **blend**.

c + at = **c**at

h + at = **h**at

ch + at = **ch**at

I Write the *ch* words you find on the chest on the lump of cheese.

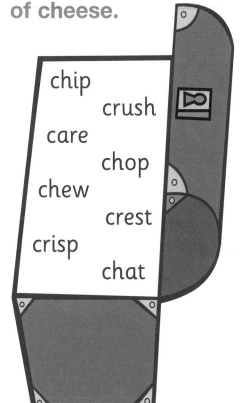

chip
crush
care
chop
chew
crest
crisp
chat

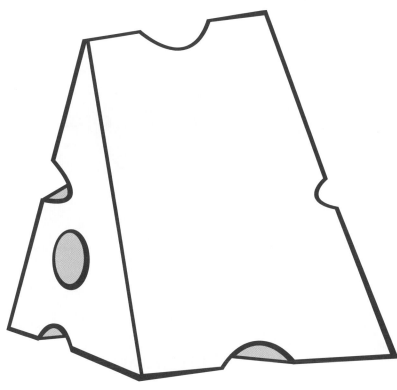

II Write *ch* to finish the words.

a _____art

b mu_____

c swit_____

d _____imp

e snat_____

f crun_____

g _____in

h lat_____

i _____at

Letter blend *sh*

When we add the letters s and h together, we make a new sound *sh*. More than one letter put together to make a sound is called a **blend**.

$$s + h = sh$$

 I Join the *sh* words to the ship with a wavy line. Then write them below.

shriek

space

spoon

ship

shin

shall

small

shave

shine

a _____ c _____ e _____

b _____ d _____ f _____

II Write *sh* to finish the words.

a _____arp   f _____ark

b _____ade   g _____in

c sma_____   h wa_____

d thra_____   i _____op

e tra_____   j wi_____

Letter blend *th*

When we add the letters *t* and *h* together, we make a new sound *th*. We have made a **blend**.

t + h = th

When we make the sound *th*, we put our tongue between our teeth and blow. Try it!

Write *th* to finish the words.

a _____ump   d _____ink   g _____is

b _____em   e _____en   h _____ese

c _____ick   f _____at   i _____ose

Choose a *th* word from the box to finish each sentence.

thump	the	then	this	think	these	thank	thick

a '_____ you!' said Julie.

b What is _____ time?

c _____ are my favourites!

d What is _____?

e _____ I came home.

f I fell down with a _____.

g My milkshake is really _____.

h I _____ I would like a cheese sandwich.

Rhymes

Do you like poems with words that rhyme? We say words rhyme when they make the same sound.

The **cat sat** on the **mat** looking at a **bat**.

Cat, **sat**, **mat** and **bat** all rhyme because they all use the sound *at*.

I Circle the word that rhymes with the word in the picture.

a cat bat   fish   dog

b book read   look   write

c door  carpet   table   floor

d wear  rip   tear   use

e hop pop   jump   pip

II Match the words so they all rhyme with their partner.

a had   b nut   c did   d red   e ball   f key   g pay   h hot

tall   hid   cut   me   bad   day   not   bed

Same sounds

Poems often have lots of words that start with the same sound. If someone wanted to write a poem about snakes, they might write about **sn**eaky **sn**akes, because both words start with the same sound – and it makes it sound as though there is a slithery snake about!

 Draw a line from each word to the word that starts with the same sound.

a smelly   b tiny   c green   d red   e big   f lovely   g dirty

lady   dog   grass   bunny   robin   skunk   toes

 Draw pictures of things that start with the same sound as the words.

a pink

b shiny

c kind

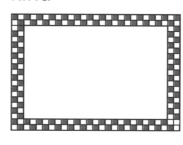

d funny

e cold

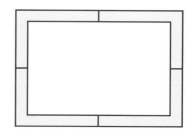

f big

25

Book language

When you talk about books, you need to be able to use 'book language'. There are special words to describe different things that you find in or on books.

I Draw a line from each word to its book part.

a title   The name of the person who wrote the book.

b author   The name of the person who drew the pictures.

c illustrator   The name of the book.

d spine   Information about the book to make you want to buy it.

e blurb   The part of the book that joins the front cover and the back cover.

 II Draw your own book cover. Include the things in the box.

title

publisher's logo

spine

blurb

front cover picture

26

Telling stories

Do you like stories? It is important that you tell them in the right order, or they do not make sense. Cinderella would be a different story if she started off rich and ended up poor and in rags!

I Read the sentences below and put them in the correct order to tell the story.

a Then they all lived happily ever after. _____

b So they chased him away with buckets of soapy water. _____

c Once upon a time, there were three little wolves who lived with their mum. _____

d The wolves knew that the pig hated to be clean. _____

e One day, a scary pig came to steal fruit from their garden. _____

II Now draw your own story by drawing pictures in the boxes below. It can be about anything you like – fairies, football, animals, space – you choose! Just make sure it is in the right order, so it makes sense.

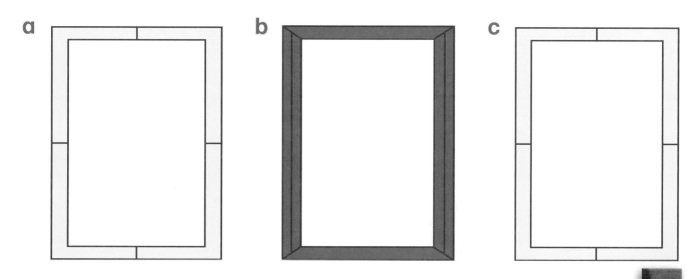

a   b   c

op words

You see the letters *op* in lots of words.

pop

shop

I Add *op* to make a word.

a t_____

b p_____

c h_____

d c_____

e b_____

f m_____

g l_____

h dr_____

i cr_____

II Draw a line from each word to its picture.

top   mop

pop   crop

hop   drop

cop   flop

bop   plop

an words

Lots of words use the letters *a* and *n* together.

man

fan

I Add *an* to make a word.

a r_____   f b_____

b t_____   g m_____

c p_____   h h_____d

d f_____   i b_____d

e c_____   j w_____d

II Draw a line from each word to its picture.

ran   man

pan   wand

fan   band

hand   orange

can   tan

at words

Lots of words end in the letter blend *at*.

hat

bat

cat

I   **Add *at* to make a word.**

a   r_____   f   h_____

b   spl_____   g   c_____

c   p_____   h   b_____

d   s_____   i   m_____

e   f_____   j   br_____

II   **Draw a line from each word to its picture.**

rat   cat

pat   bat

sat   mat

fat   chat

hat   bat

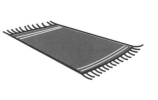

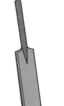

ip words

You will see the letters *ip* in lots of words.

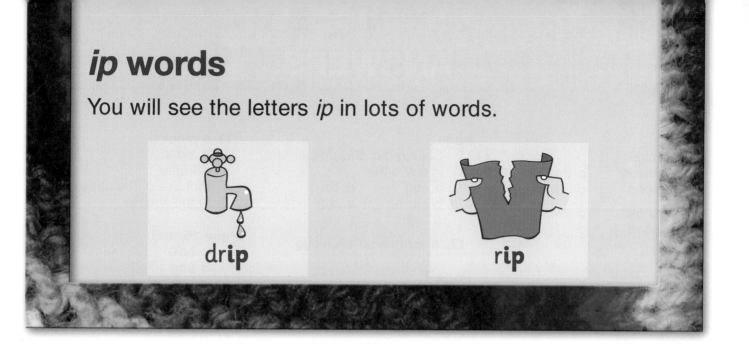

dr**ip**

r**ip**

I   **Add *ip* to make a word.**

a   r_____   f   h_____

b   t_____   g   l_____

c   p_____   h   n_____

d   s_____   i   dr_____

e   d_____   j   sl_____

II   **Circle the words that end in *ip*.**

a   rip   rap   roll

b   top   toll   tip

c   pop   pull   pip

d   sat   sip   sap

e   dog   dip   dig

f   hop   hall   hip

g   lip   lap   lot

h   nip   nap   not

ANSWERS

Page 2
I Circled:
    a sheep   **c** swan
    b scarf   **d** shirt

II **a** snake   **c** swing
    b soap

Page 3
I Coloured:
    a apple   **c** ant
    b acorn   **d** alligator

II 'a' written on all the apples

Page 4
I Circled:
    a ink   **f** in
    b ice cream **g** idea
    c island   **h** ill
    d iron   **i** icy
    e ivy   **j** itch

II **a** pink   **d** drill
    b bin   **e** stink
    c milk   **f** idea

Page 5
I Circled:
    a train   **c** television
    b tiger   **d** table

II 't' written in train carriages

Page 6
I Circled:
    a play   **f** post
    b pool   **g** paw
    c pink   **h** pen
    d pipe   **i** pencil
    e pan, plate **j** plants

II **a** pink   **f** pull
    b pat   **g** spell
    c help   **h** pitch
    d put   **i** pot
    e copy   **j** pit

Page 7
I

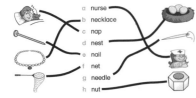

II 'n' written on each bead

Page 8
I Coloured and words written
   in any order:
    a egg   **d** ear
    b earth   **e** eat
    c eight   **f** eel

II 'e' written on each egg

Page 9
I Pictures drawn as asked.

II Words copied correctly.

Page 10
I Words written in any order:
    a ugly   **d** uncle
    b up   **e** us
    c under

II Words written in any order
   on umbrellas.

Page 11
I Words copied onto mice in
   any order:
    a out   **d** our
    b odd   **e** oar
    c old   **f** ocean

II **a** sold   **f** pop
    b spot   **g** box
    c cold   **h** work
    d world   **i** bow
    e money

Page 12
I Circled: medal, monkey,
   map, mud, mouse. Words
   written in any order.

II 6 things starting with the
   letter *m*.

Page 13
I **a** rain   **d** rabbit
   b rope   **e** rice
   c red   **f** run

II 6 things beginning with *r*.

Page 14
I Joined (then written in any
   order):
    a kiss   **d** kit
    b key   **e** kind
    c kettle   **f** kite

II **a** clock
    b kitten
    c kettle
   Pictures of the above drawn
   in the spaces.

Page 15
I **a** boy
    b bad
    c bat
    d bus
    e bug

II **a** tub   **f** bin
    b box   **g** bob
    c bend   **h** job
    d bank   **i** bun
    e baby

Page 16
I Joined (and the words then
   written in any order):
    a drum   **d** duck
    b dress   **e** doll
    c deer   **f** door

II **a** made   **f** doll
    b shed   **g** card
    c disc   **h** desk
    d body   **i** handle
    e drain

Page 17
I *l* written on each leaf.

II Items ticked as child shows
   them to an adult.

Page 18
I

II Anything that starts with the
   letter *f*, drawn on the shapes
   and then written, i.e. fox,
   finger, face.